The Pride Street Crew
10
Let's Go Shopping

Mike Wilson

Published in association with
The Basic Skills Agency

Acknowledgements
Cover: Jim Eldridge
Illustrations: Jim Eldridge

Orders; please contact Bookpoint Ltd, 39 Milton Park, Abingdon, Oxon OX14
4TD. Telephone: (44) 01235 400414, Fax: (44) 01235 400454. Lines are open
from 9.00–6.00, Monday to Saturday, with a 24 hour message answering service.
Email address: orders@bookpoint.co.uk

British Library Cataloguing in Publication Data
A catalogue record for this title is available from the British Library

ISBN 0 340 77632 3

First published 2000
Impression number 10 9 8 7 6 5 4 3 2 1
Year   2005 2004 2003 2002 2001 2000

Copyright © 2000 Mike Wilson

Typeset by GreenGate Publishing Services, Tonbridge, Kent.
Printed in Great Britain for Hodder and Stoughton Educational, a division of
Hodder Headline Plc, 338 Euston Road, London NW1 3BH, by Atheneum
Press, Gateshead, Tyne & Wear

JOHN / BONE

WESLEY / TALL

LUKE / SKY

SIMON / CUSTARD

CARL / SPOT

It's Saturday.

At 12 o'clock,
Uncle Gary gives me an hour off.

I go and meet Lizzy.
I want to go
and get a bite to eat.

But Lizzy wants to go shopping.

First it's tops.

She picks about ten tops.

A little red one.
A little black one.
A shiny one.
They all look the same.

She goes and tries them on.

'How about this one, Luke?'

'Yeah,' I say. 'Fine.'

'Or how about the green one?'

'Fine,' I say.

'Does the red one go
with the skirt I got last week?'

I say, 'Yes, it's fine.'

Then it's hats.

Lizzy wants a hat.

'Does this one go with my eyes?'
she says.

'I don't know!' I say.
I'm hungry.
I want my dinner.

'What does my hair look like in this one?'
asks Lizzy.

'It looks like hair!' I say.

I stand round the shop
with the other boys.
And some men.

We try not to look each other
in the eye.

We all know
we've got years of this in front of us.

Now Lizzy is in a mood.

'You're not helping …' she says.

'Well I hate shopping!' I say.
'It's a waste of time,
and a waste of money.'

I push past her.

'I'm going back to work,' I say.

Lizzy throws down the hat she's got on.
She comes after me.

Outside the shop,
Lizzy grabs my arm.

'Wait, Luke!'

She pulls at me –
then stops.

'What's that?' she says.
'On your hand …'

'Oh, nothing.'

She's seen Tamsin Taylor's name
and phone number.
Tamsin put it on my hand
yesterday.
It hasn't washed off yet.

Lizzy steps back.
She folds her arms.

'So are you seeing Tamsin Taylor now?'

'No,' I say.
'She was just messing about.'

Lizzy says,
'And when were you going to tell me?
About the two of you ...'

'Look, Lizzy,' I say.
'It's not what you think.
It's you I want.
Not Tamsin. Not anyone.
I want to go out with you'.

'I just don't want to go shopping with you
all the time …'

But Lizzy won't listen.
She looks at me,
like I'm something sticky
she just stepped in.

'My Mum was right about you,'
is all she says.

Then I have to get back to work.

I get a dead funny look from my Uncle Ray.

'Young lady came looking for you,'
he says.

'She said to call her on her mobile.
She said you've got her number.'

After work,
I find a phone box
on my way home.

'Hello, Mrs Lawson.
Can I speak to Lizzy, please?'

(I can be such a nice boy when I try!)

I wait a long time.
Her hand is over the phone.
Then Lizzy's Mum says,

'No.'

'Is Lizzy there, Mrs Lawson?'

Another long wait.

Then,

'No.'

I put the phone down,
and call Tamsin.

Her number is still there,
where she wrote it.
In the palm of my hand.

You kiss a girl, right?
And you think you know it all.

But then you kiss another girl ...
and the way she kisses is ...

It's the same,
and not the same ...
all at the same time.

Do you know what I mean?

I'm not proud of Tamsin.
What we did.

Maybe it's all part of growing up.
Doing new things.
Trying things out.

I don't know.

I felt bad about Lizzy.
I felt good about Tamsin.
It was as simple as that.
I didn't think about it much.

Until that Sunday,
when I saw Shane Green.

Shane was not in the Pride Street Crew.
But he was OK.
He was at school with us.

When he saw me
we always did a high-five.

'Hey Luke! Give me five!'

And slap our hands together.

It's Sunday,
the day after me and Tamsin.

I see Shane in the park.

'Hey, Luke!' Shane says. 'Give me five!'

Shane goes to slap hands with me.
And in the palm of his hand,
I see Tamsin's name.
Her name and phone number.

She must have put them there
yesterday.
Just before she put them on my hand.
Or just after.

I feel sick.
I feel stupid.

Shane tells me they didn't do anything.
Tamsin was just messing about, he says.

But now I know how it feels.
Now I know how Lizzy must be feeling.

So I go round to see Lizzy.

I've got to say I'm sorry.

Lizzy's Mum says she's busy.
'You can't come in,' she says.
'It's her driving theory test next week ...'

But Mrs Lawson must be feeling sorry for me.

She goes and gets Lizzy.

I wait.

I'm thinking,
it was so stupid –
the way we fell out.

It was just about shopping.
And then the Tamsin thing.

But that's over now.
Well and truly over.

When she comes to the door,
Lizzy doesn't say anything.
Just looks at me, arms folded.

'I came to say …' I begin.

But then I dry up.

What can I say?

'Sorry?' No.

'I love you?' No way.

'I've been stupid and selfish?' No.

That won't work.

So I say,

'We could go shopping,
I'll come with you …
I'll help …
You can buy shoes … and tops …'

'That's sweet of you, Luke,' says Lizzy.
'I'll think about it.'

She starts to close the door.
'I've got some stuff to do now,' she says.
'Bye bye.'

So I go home.

I don't know if we'll get back together.
Lizzy said she'd think about it.
So maybe there is hope.

Maybe I said the right thing.
About shopping.

I hate shopping.
Well, I hate *girly* shopping,
you know?

But I can put up with it,
if it means
I can get Lizzy back.